DANIEL O'DONNELL

3/4

Exclusive Distributors:
Music Sales Limited, 8/9 Frith Street, London W1V 5TZ, England.
Music Sales Pty Limited, 120 Rothschild Avenue, Rosebery, NSW 2018, Australia.

This book © Copyright 1991 by Wise Publications.
Order No.AM86490
ISBN 0.7119.2788.X

Compiled by Pat Conway. Music processed by Seton Music Graphics.

Music Sales' complete catalogue lists thousands of titles and is free from your local music shop, or direct from Music Sales Limited.
Please send a cheque/postal order for £1.50 for postage to: Music Sales Limited, Newmarket Road, Bury St. Edmunds, Suffolk IP33 3YB.

Your Guarantee of Quality: As publishers, we strive to produce every book to the highest commercial standards.
All the music has been freshly engraved and the book has been carefully designed to minimise awkward page turns and to
make playing from it a real pleasure. Particular care has been given to specifying acid-free, neutral-sized paper which
has not been chlorine bleached but produced with special regard for the environment.
Throughout, the printing and binding have been planned to ensure a sturdy, attractive publication which should give years of enjoyment.
If your copy fails to meet our high standards, please inform us and we will gladly replace it.
Unauthorised reproduction of any part of this publication by any means including photocopying is an infringement of copyright.

Printed in the United Kingdom by
J.B. Offset Printers (Marks Tey) Limited, Marks Tey, Essex.

WISE PUBLICATIONS
London / New York / Sydney

BED OF ROSES

Words & Music by Harold Reid.

1. She was called the scar-let wo-man by the

peo-ple___ who would go to church but left me in the street. With no

par-ents of my own___ I ne-ver had a home and an eight-teen year old boy has got to

eat. She found me out - side Sun - day morn - ing___ beg - ging

mon - ey from a man I did - n't know. She took me in and wiped a - way my

child - hood. A la - dy of the street this wo - man Rose. This

Chorus

bed of ro - ses that I lay on,___ where I was taught to be a

3

2. She was a handsome woman just thirty five
   Who was spoken to in town by very few.
   She managed a late evening business
   Like most of the town wished they could do.
   And I learned all the things that a man should know
   From a woman not approved of I suppose
   But she died knowing that I really loved her
   From life's bramble bush I picked a rose.

   Chorus:—

   Repeat Chorus:—

BLUE EYES CRYING IN THE RAIN

Words & Music by Fred Rose.

In the twi - light glow I__ see you.__

Blue eyes cry - ing__ in the rain.__

When we kissed good-bye and par - ted____ I

knew____ we'd ne - ver____ meet a - gain.

Love is like____ a dy - ing em - ber.____

On - ly me - mo - ries____ re - main.

Through the a - ges___ I'll re - mem - ber___

Blue eyes cry - ing___ in the rain. rain.___

___ Blue eyes cry - ing___ in the rain.___

2. Now my hair has turned to silver
   All my life I've loved in vain
   I can see your star in heaven
   Blue eyes crying in the rain.
   Some day when we meet up yonder
   We'll stroll hand in hand again
   In a land that knows no parting
   Blue eyes crying in the rain.

DON'T BE ANGRY

Words & Music by Wade Jackson.

© Copyright 1954 Acuff-Rose Music Incorporated, USA.
Acuff-Rose Opryland Music Limited, 129 Park Street, London W1.
All Rights Reserved. International Copyright Secured.

1. Don't be angry___ with me dar - ling___ if I fail to un - der -

-stand all___ your lit - tle___ whims and wishes___ all_____ the

2. When I recall the first time that I flirted with you dear,
   When I jokingly said "Come and be my wife,"
   Now time has turned the pages it's the sweetest joke on earth
   That I have you dear, forever by my side.

3. Maybe someday you're gonna hurt me, I've been hurt in love before
   Only God can know and time alone will tell
   But in the meantime I'll keep loving you with all my head and soul
   And pray God to let it last if it's his will.

4. *Repeat first verse.*

DON'T FORGET TO REMEMBER ME

Words & Music by Barry Gibb & Maurice Gibb.

can't   get my - self   ov - er   you.   Don't for -

Chorus

-get   to   re - mem - ber   me   and the love   that used   to   be.

I   still re - mem - ber you   I___   love you.___   In   my

heart   lies   a mem - or - y   to tell   the stars   a -

2. On my wall lies a photograph of you girl
   Though I try to forget you somehow
   You're the mirror of my soul
   So take me out of my hole
   Let me try to go on living right now.

   Chorus:—

I DON'T CARE

Words & Music by Buck Owens.

tops don't spin   I don't care if the gins won't gin   Just   as

long   as   you love____ me.   So dar - ling let it____ rain,

let it____ snow,   let the cold   north wind blow,   just   as

long   as   you love____ me.   North   or   south,____

2. Well I don't care if the birds don't sing
   I don't care if the bells don't ring
   Just as long as you love me
   And I don't care if the world don't turn
   I don't care if the fires won't burn
   Just as long as you love me.

   Chorus:—

IRISH EYES

Words & Music by Hank Locklin & George Carroll.

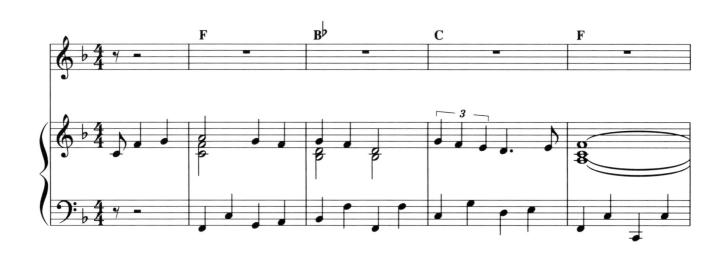

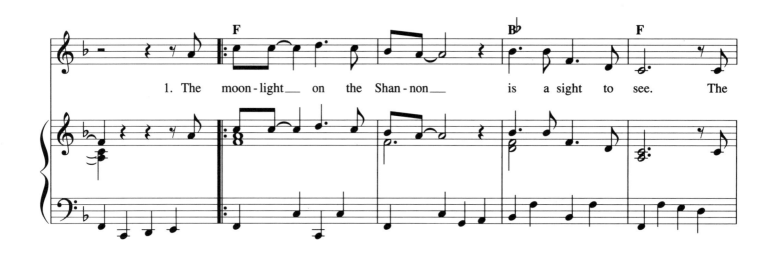

1. The moon-light__ on the Shan-non__ is a sight to see. The

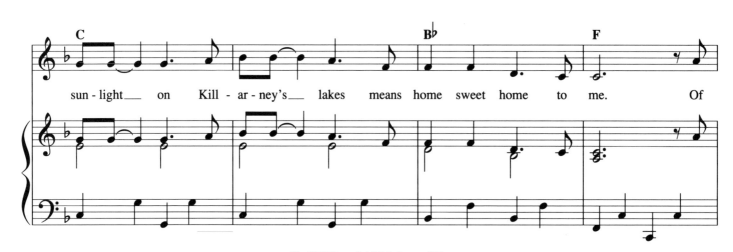

sun-light__ on Kill-ar-ney's__ lakes means home sweet home to me. Of

2.	To stroll again Antrim's Glens and see the waterfall.
	To sleep beneath the mystic hills in dear old Donegal.
	Or walk the shores of Eireann and hear the seagulls cry.
	But most of all to look into your lovely Irish eyes.

3. To hear again those Shandon bells ringing heavenly
	Beside the laughing waters of the lovely Lee.
	Or listen to the ocean and the wind that sighs
	But most of all to see again your smiling Irish eyes.

4. In dreams I see your angel face that aches my lonely heart
	The memory when I told you we would have to part
	I can't forget that morning when we said goodbye
	I can't forget those tear drops in your Irish eyes
	I love you and I need you, my lovely Irish eyes.

I NEED YOU

Words & Music by Baker Knight.

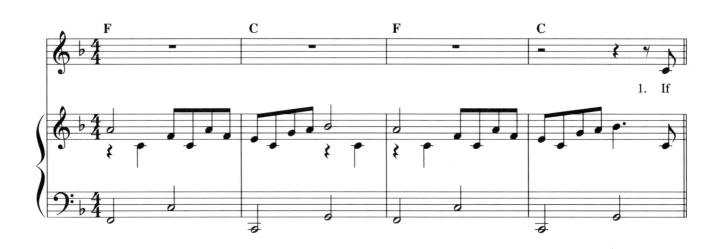

1. If

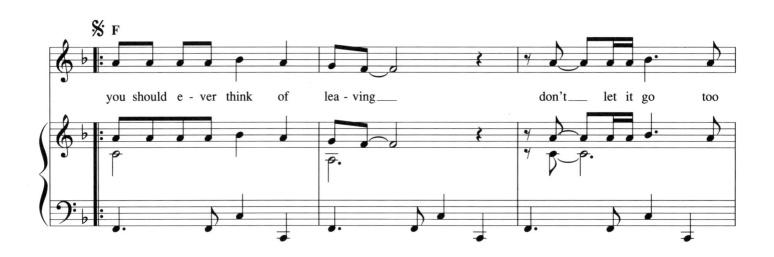

you should e-ver think of lea-ving___ don't___ let it go too

far. The love___ of a life-time,___ Dar-ling that's what you

are.   And now___ that I've found you   I'll be count - ing on

you   to love me___ for - ev - er,___ 'Cos I need you___ hon - est___ I

do.   do.   It took an aw - ful lot of look - ing___ to find you,___

Oh what a time I've been through.   'Cos dar - ling it's not ve - ry ea - sy___

2. Every single day my love for you
   Keeps growing more and more.
   The lips of an angel
   Never kissed me before
   And now that I've found you
   I'll be counting on you.
   No man is an island
   And I need you, honest I do.

3. Two of us together hand in hand
   We stand at heaven's door
   Together forever
   I'll be yours evermore
   And now that I've found you
   I'll be counting on you
   To love me forever
   'Cos I need you, honest I do.

MY SHOES KEEP WALKING BACK TO YOU

Words & Music by Ross & Wills.

when the day is___ through.___ My heart-aches___ start a-new and

that's when I___ miss you___ most of all.___ And my

Chorus

arms_____ keep reach-ing for you_____ And my

eyes_____ keep search-ing for you._____ My____

2. No matter how much I pretend
   I wish I had you back again
   For nothing else means half as much as you
   Our world just seemed to die
   The day you said goodbye
   And I can't forget no matter what I do.

   Chorus:—

SECOND FIDDLE

Words & Music by Buck Owens.

I play sec-ond fid-dle to your new love while it lasts. Just like all the o-thers I played for in the past, Why can't I be a lea-der and play a lea-ding part? Why must I al-ways

2. Each time you find a new love
   You leave me here to cry
   Teardrops tell a story
   Of a love that just won't die.
   Like an early morning paper
   The news you get just part
   Why must I always have to play
   Second fiddle in your heart.

   Chorus:—

   Repeat Chorus:—

STAND BESIDE ME

Words & Music by Thomas P. Glaser.

Stand be- -side me, stand be - side me. For if

I should lose you I just could - n't___ get any___ where.___ Stand be-

-side me, stand be - side me. You're the

only one who ev-er___ made me care.

1.I can't stand to think___ that I might___ be a-lone___

Not a-lone a-gain,___ not the

way it was back then, be-fore you walked in-to my___ heart. Told me

2. There'll be times when everything goes wrong
   But darling I won't care if I know you're standing there
   No matter what we have to do
   Together we can see it through
   So stand beside me and I'll be standing
   Right there next to you.

   Chorus:—

THAT'S A SAD AFFAIR

Words & Music by Redd Stewart.

2. She always follows him around next door and back again.
If she can't be his lady fair she'll be his in the end
'Cos she just wants to be with him no matter when or where
She's given up her paper dolls and now she totes a gun
'Cos that's the way he likes to play so she pretends it's fun
For him she'd do 'most anything but he's so unaware,
For he's just four and she's just three and it's a sad affair.

When the rain comes falling down and they must be apart
It doesn't bother him at all but it almost breaks her heart
She's just content to tag along in the hope some day he'll care
But he's just four and she's just three and that's a sad affair.

THE STREETS OF BALTIMORE

Words & Music by Harlan Howard & Thomas P. Glaser.

sold my __ farm to take my __ wo-man __ where she longed __ to be. I

left my __ kin __ and all my __ friends __ back there in __ Ten-nes-see. I

bought those___ one - way tic - kets___ she had of - ten begged___ me for,___ and they

took us___ to___ the streets of___ Bal - ti - more. Her

heart was filled with laugh - ter___ when she saw those___ ci - ty lights. She

said the pret - ti - est___ place on earth___ is Bal - ti - more at___ night. Well a

man feels proud to give his___ wo - man___ what she's long - ing___ for and I

tried to like___ the streets of___ Bal - ti - more._____ -more.

yes my ba - by___ walks the streets of___ Bal - ti - more._____

2. I got myself a factory job
I ran an old machine.
I bought a little cottage
In a neighbourhood serene.
And every night that I came home
With every muscle sore
She would drag me through
The streets of Baltimore
Well I tried hard to bring her back
To where she used to be
But I soon learned she loved those bright lights
More than she loved me.
Well I'm going back on that same train
That brought me here before
While my baby walks
The streets of Baltimore.

VEIL OF WHITE LACE

Words & Music by Damon Black.

that she'd change her mind._____ There were

beau - ti _ - ful ro - ses in a bri - dal bou -

quet_____ where she stood at___ the al -

tar_____ in a veil of white lace._____

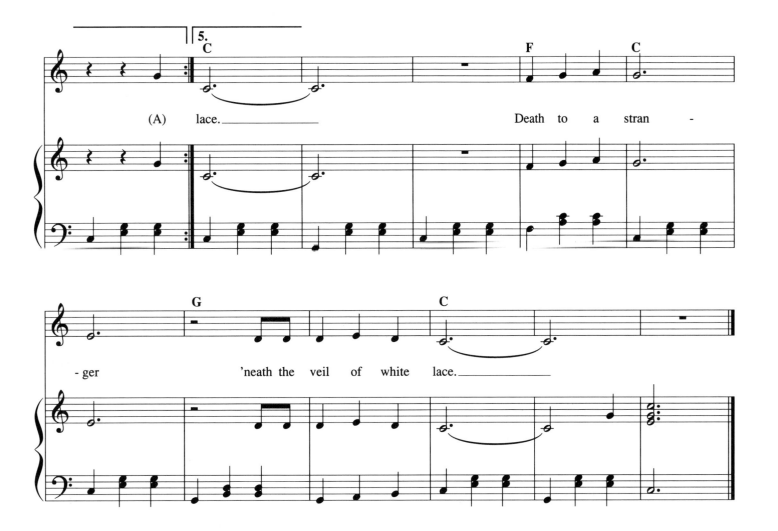

2. A stranger in silence reached out for her hand
   And placed on her finger a gold wedding band
   There was happiness written in a smile on his face
   But I couldn't see her for the veil of white lace.

3. I pitied the stranger for all he could see
   Was their life together for eternity
   My heart filled with anger as I pictured the face
   Of a false-hearted crittur 'neath the veil of white lace.

4. I reached in my pocket when the wedding was done
   My hand touched a locket then fell on the gun
   It shattered the silence as it left its trace
   Stains of red crimson on the veil of white lace.

5. I ran from the church house as I threw down the gun
   But stopped at the doorstep where there, crossing the lawn,
   My darling said she had decided to wait
   Death to a stranger 'neath the veil of white lace.

WEDDING BELLS

Words & Music by Claude Boone.

Chorus

hap - py____ just the same. Wed - ding____ bells____ are

ring - ing____ in the cha - pel that should be____ ring - ing

out for you and me. Down the aisle with

some - one____ else____ you're walk - ing. Those wed - ding____ bells____ will

2. I planned a little cottage in the valley
I even bought a little band of gold
I thought someday I'd place it on your finger
But now the future looks so dark and cold.

Chorus:—Wedding bells are ringing in the chapel.
I hear the children laughing now with glee.
At home alone I hang my head in sorrow
Those wedding bells will never ring for me.

3. I fancy I can see a bunch of roses
A blossom from an orange tree in your hair
While the organ plays I love you truly
Please let me pretend that I am there.

Chorus:—Wedding bells are ringing in the chapel
Ever since the day you set me free
Down the aisle with someone else you're walking
But wedding bells will never ring for me.

13231 3/92